The
Carl
Larsson

COLORING
BOOK

*With paintings
selected and redrawn*

by Andy Nelson

Culpepper Press

MINNEAPOLIS

A Note to Parents, Grandparents, Teachers and Friends of Children...

Here's how you can help your child make the most of this book:

1. Read the introduction, so you can answer the basic questions your child may ask about Carl Larsson.

2. Browse through the pages with your child, discussing the pictures, asking which he or she wishes to color first. Read the titles to the child. Note the suggestions and questions (on the left hand pages) intended to encourage the child to produce original drawings using his or her own imagination. Stimulate that imagination with discussions and questions of your own.

3. Ask your child, "Would you like me to color with you?"

4. Provide crayons and suggest other tools: colored pencils, fine point markers, watercolor paints. Take a moment to introduce these new tools to the child, showing him or her the distinctive marks each tool makes. Show how to care for these tools. Please comply if your child wishes to try watercolors, but indicate the responsibility of laying down newspaper, gently cleaning brushes with soap and warm water, etc.

5. Don't criticize what to you appears messy or nonsensical coloring. Allow your child's self-expressive and personal color choices.

6. Take your child to the library to check out books by and about Carl Larsson. Find and compare the original paintings to those reproduced in this book.

7. Visit a Scandinavian museum or gift shop. Help the child select a Carl Larsson greeting card, poster or calendar. Point out other traditional Scandinavian items and designs. If your child is not Scandinavian, encourage exploration of his or her own cultural heritage.

8. As your child grows, follow up this introduction to Carl Larsson with other appropriate and complementary gifts. From such childhood experiences grow fond memories, personal histories and treasured artifacts.

A child whose activities are directed with loving encouragement, whose experiments are designed to succeed, will develop greater self-esteem, creativity and stick-to-it-tiveness than will the unguided child left alone to his or her devices. —*Andy Nelson*

About the author:

ANDY NELSON is the author/illustrator of Culpepper Press's critically acclaimed *Impressionists Coloring Book*, as well as the illustrator of their popular children's book, *A Is For At Bat: A Baseball Primer*. He is the staff artist for *The Minneapolis Review of Baseball* and is also a mural artist. He is a graduate of Bemidji State University and is a former public school art teacher. He has two daughters and lives in Minneapolis, where he is working on upcoming children's books. Like Carl Larsson, he is of 100% Scandinavian descent.

For my grandparents:
Annie Christianson and Allen Foster, Edna Thorpe and the late Thome Nelson, all of Oklee, Minnesota.

My thanks to May at the Swedish Consulate, Minneapolis; Eva and Annette at the American Swedish Institute, Minneapolis, and to Kerstin at the Swedish American Museum Center, Chicago.

Cover paintings by Carl Larsson: front, *Brita and I* and *Karin and Kersti*; back, *Ulf and Pontus*. Reproduced with permission of the Göteborgs Konstmuseum, Göteborg, Sweden. Title page: *Brita and I*, 1895; Konstmuseum, Goteborg.

ISBN 0-939636-07-4   10 9 8 7 6 5 4 3 2 1

CULPEPPER PRESS, 2901 Fourth Street S.E., Minneapolis, Minnesota 55414

Culpepper Press books are available to organizations at quantity discounts.
Write for information.

Introduction

In his own words he was a "poor little neglected wretch, ugly and regarded as stupid, always in the way at home and never welcomed abroad; in fact quite browbeaten." Born May 28, 1853 in Gamla Stan, the old part of Stockholm, Sweden, Larsson was descended from peasants and craftsmen.

Recommended by a teacher from the "poor school," Carl was accepted into Stockholm's Royal Academy of Fine Art at age 13. When he graduated, he was earning 2500 kr. a year (more than the head of the Academy) as an illustrator for *Punch* magazine. During the 1870s he illustrated many books, including Hans Christian Andersen's "Fairy Tales." In 1876 he won the Royal Medal, the Academy's highest honor, but that spring a fellow student, Vilhelmina Holmgren, died while giving birth to hers and Carl's second child. Depressed, Carl left Sweden for Paris soon after.

Eventually he moved to the countryside of Grèz-sur-Loing, a haven for transplanted Scandinavian artists. There he stayed three years, turning from oil painting to more intimate open-air watercolors. "I looked at nature for the first time. I chucked the bizarre into the trash-heap . . . " he wrote. "The pregnant, lusty earth is now going to be the theme of my painting." Carl won a medal at the Paris Salon, sold works to the French government, Swedish Nationalmuseum, and to collectors. His work showed influences from Impressionist, Japanese, and Rococo artists.

In Grèz, Carl met Karin Bergoo. Six years his junior, she also had graduated from Stockholm's Royal Academy. Unlike Carl, she came from a well-to-do, prestigious family.

Karin and Carl were married in Sweden in 1883. They returned to Grèz, where in 1884, Suzanne was born, the first of eight children. As Carl's art became more popular back home, he asked himself, "Why in the name of all that's blue-green not paint Swedish nature in Sweden itself?!" Thus in 1885, Karin and Carl returned to Sweden for good.

In 1888, Karin's father gave the couple a small cottage in Sundborn. This became "Little Hyttnas" (the hut on a point), the most familiar home in the nation, and the source of Carl Larsson's artistic legacy. Karin forsook her art career to further develop Carl's vision of the domestic ideal.

Carl saw color printing as a way to reach more people with his art. When it rained for six straight weeks during the summer of 1894, Karin recommended he depict their home in "souvenir pictures." Carl boldly suggested that these pictures serve as "a guide for people who feel the need to fix up their homes in a nice way." The Carl Larsson look thus became the Swedish standard.

Carl wrote "these are the happy and charming scenes that are played all the time under my own eyes." In reality, they were excruciatingly staged under Karin's guiding eye. She made sure that everywhere Carl looked within the ever-expanding cottage would be a potential vignette for a harmonious composition. Abandoning her own painting, Karin accepted the equally demanding assignment as her husband's art director, stage designer and costumer.

When mural work at the Nationalmuseum damaged his eyesight and political squabblings surrounding the commission affected his nerves, Carl began suffering severe headaches. Although his 50th birthday in 1903 was celebrated as a national holiday, Carl's disillusionments returned. 'Being in Stockholm is like walking in a jungle full of malicious apes and horrid serpents." In 1905, son Ulf, 18, died during an appendectomy. In 1908 an old friend, August Strindberg, publically proclaimed that the Larssons were simply putting on a show—that beneath the facade were actually two despicable personalities. Others claimed theirs was a love-hate relationship, motivated only by their common desire for fame.

In 1910 Carl completed another controversial mural at the Nationalmuseum: "Midvinterblot" was met with great criticism. His always-shaky self esteem continued to erode.

The last years of his life were spent more peacefully. His painting, chiefly commissioned portraits, was interspersed with work on his memoirs, which he completed in the fall of 1918. His eyesight continued to worsen, and in January of 1919, he suffered a minor stroke. One evening, he and Karin were listening to their daughters sing and play the piano when Carl, with unbearable pain in his head, left for his bedroom with Karin, whom he told,"It feels so strange, I think I'm dying." That night, January 22, 1919, Carl Larsson died.

In the 1970s, due partly to a wave of nostalgia, Carl Larsson's work was rediscovered. Today his paintings are more popular than ever. His genius is appreciated.

—*Andy Nelson*

LITTLE SUZANNE, Oil, 1885
from *Larssons*, 1902
Konstmuseum, Göteborg
This is Carl and Karin's first child. What do you think your children will look like?

ULF AND PONTUS, 1894
Konstmuseum, Göteborg
Ulf and Pontus are pretending they are Royal Guards.
What is your favorite make-believe thing to do?

THE CRAYFISH SEASON OPENS, (Detail), c. 1894–1897
from *Ett Hem*, 1899
Nationalmuseum, Stockholm
What do you think a crayfish looks like? Use your imagination.

LISBETH, 1894
Konstmuseum, Göteborg
What do you think could be making Lisbeth laugh?

NAME DAY AT THE STORAGE SHED, c. 1894–97
from *Ett Hem*, 1899
Nationalmuseum, Stockholm
How would you dress up so that no one in the world could recognize you?

THE OTHER HALF OF THE STUDIO, c. 1894–97
from *Ett Hem*, 1899
Nationalmuseum, Stockholm
What tools will you use if you become an artist someday?

SELF-PORTRAIT, 1895
Prince Eugen's Waldemarsudde, Stockholm
Carl Larsson was 42 years old at this time. Was the artist left-handed? Why do you or don't you think
so? Can you draw your self-portrait on this page? What would you show yourself doing?

SEEN IN THE MIRROR, 1895
from *Larssons*, 1902
Privately owned
Now can you tell if Carl Larsson is left-handed or right-handed?
Can you draw yourself by looking in a mirror?

THE BRIDGE, 1896
from *Ett Hem*, 1899
Can you draw the most fantastic bridge you can imagine? What would it cross over?

KARIN AND KERSTI, 1898
Konstmuseum, Göteborg
Carl and Karin Larsson had eight children: Suzanne, Ulf, Pontus, Lisbeth, Matts (who was just three months old when he died), Brita, Kersti and Esbjorn. Can you draw your family tree?

HIDE AND SEEK, 1898
from *Larssons*, 1902
Where is your favorite place to hide?

FOR KARIN'S NAME-DAY, 1899
The Carl Larsson Farm, Sundborn
What do you think a "name-day" is? If you don't know, where do you think you could find out?

A LATE-RISER'S MISERABLE BREAKFAST, 1900
from *Larssons*, 1902
What do you think the other children are doing while the late-riser sits alone at the table?

ESBJORN, NOVEMBER, 1900
from *Larssons*, 1902
Konstmuseum, Göteborg
Do you remember some of your favorite toys from when you were a baby?

BRITA AS IDUN ("Brita with the Christmas Apples"), Lithograph, 1901
Title sketch of *Idun*'s 1901 Christmas issue after a Carl Larsson watercolor
What do you suppose is the color of Brita's dress? Can you draw your favorite holiday costume?

SUZANN' AND ANOTHER 'ANN, 1901
Privately owned
What would the wallpaper in your room look like if it could be anything you want?

ESBJORN AND GRANDPA, 1902
Frontispiece to *Larssons*, 1902
Grandpa is serving as a model in front of a large canvas in the studio.
What memory can you draw of your grandparents?

BARBRO, 1903
from *Andras Barn*, 1913
Do you recognize the painting behind Barbro? Where else have you seen it?
Can you draw your brother or sister, or a friend?

"OUTDOORS BLOW THE SUMMER WINDS . . . ", (Detail) Oil, 1903
Latinlaroverket (Classical High School, now Hvitfeldska Gymnasiet), Göteborg
Who are some of the interesting characters you would see on the street or road in front of your home?

"OUTDOORS BLOW THE SUMMER WINDS . . . ", (Detail) Oil, 1903
Latinlaroverket (Classical High School, now Hvitfeldska Gymnasiet), Göteborg
Who would you never expect to see on the street or road in front of your house?

ESBJORN, FISHING, 1903
from *De Mina*, 1919
How many different kinds of fish can you draw for Esbjorn to catch?

"STAR BOYS" CALL AT LARSSONS', 1904
from *De Mina*, 1919
Can you draw your favorite Halloween costume?

THE MANURE PILE, c. 1904
from *Spadarvet*, 1906
Albert Bonniers Förlag, Stockholm
What machinery does a modern farmer use? What crops or animals would you raise if you were a farmer?

IN THE CARPENTER SHOP, c. 1904
from *Spadarvet*, 1906
Albert Bonniers Förlag, Stockholm
What tools would a modern carpenter use?

JOHANNA MILKING, c. 1904
from *Spadarvet*, 1906
How many foods can you draw that are made from milk?

SPRING HARROWING, c. 1904
from *Spadarvet*, 1906
What other services did horses provide in the olden days?

DIGGING POTATOES, c. 1904
from *Spadarvet*, 1906
What favorite foods would you plant in your garden?

FISHING (c. 1905)
from *Spadarvet*, 1906
Albert Bonniers Förlag, Stockholm
What would the boat look like that you would like to ride in?

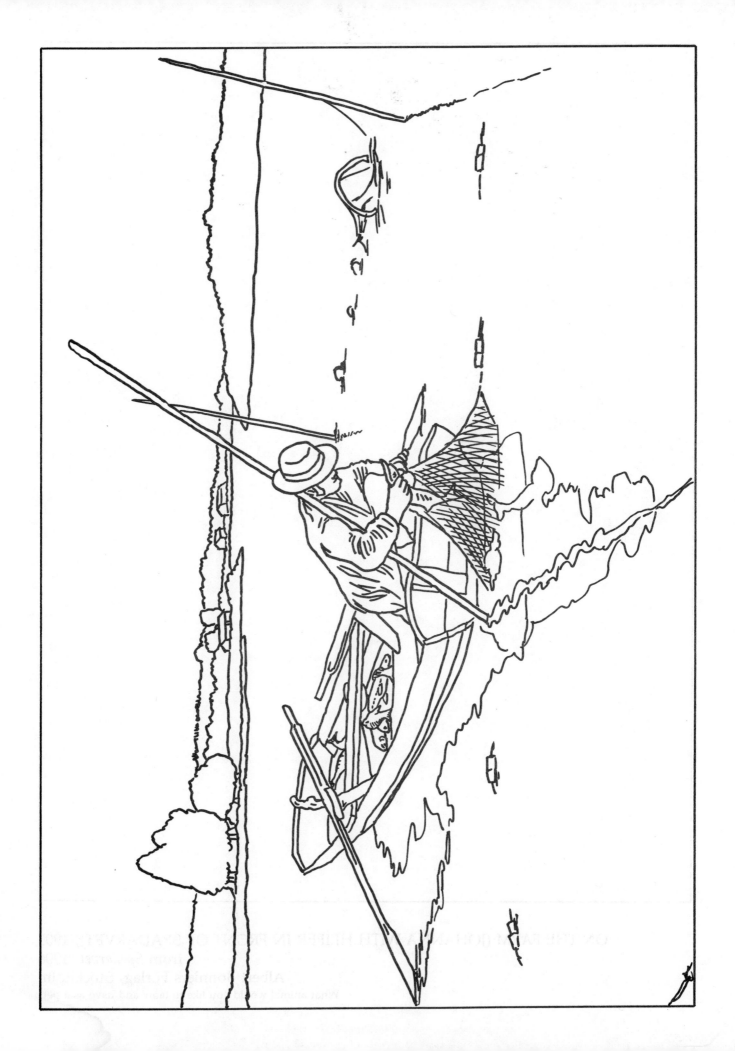

ON THE FARM (JOHANNA WITH HEIFER IN FRONT OF SPADARVET), 1905
from *Spadarvet*, 1906
Albert Bonniers Förlag, Stockholm
What animal would you like to tame and have as a pet?

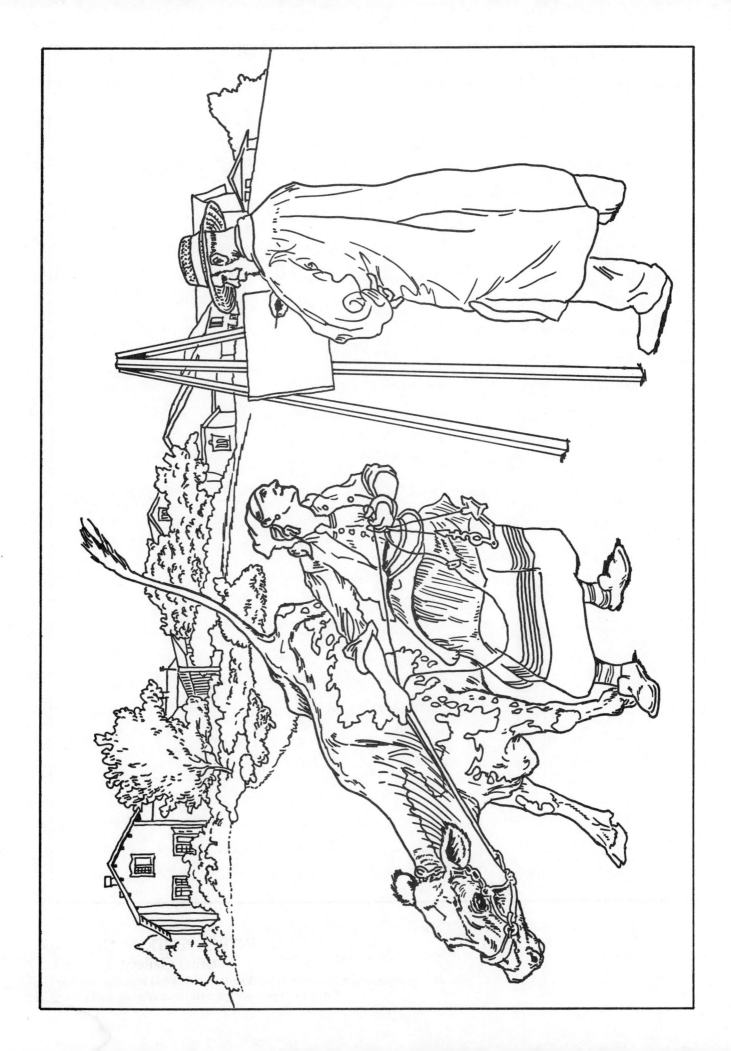

INTROSPECTION, Oil, 1906
Uffizi Gallery, Florence
Why do you suppose Carl Larsson is holding this doll? Who is at the window?
Can you draw yourself with your favorite doll or toy?

CARPENTER HELLBERG'S CHILDREN, 1906
Konstmuseum, Göteborg
What kinds of toys do you think a carpenter would make for his children?

NOW IT'S CHRISTMAS AGAIN, Oil, 1907
Left panel of Triptych
Museum, Helsingborg
This, and the next two drawings, are part of an oil painting called a triptych. This means that these
three pictures form a larger picture when placed side by side. Can you draw your grandmother?

NOW IT'S CHRISTMAS AGAIN, Oil, 1907
Center panel of Triptych
Museum, Helsingborg
What would your favorite plate of food from a family holiday dinner look like?

NOW IT'S CHRISTMAS AGAIN, Oil, 1907
Right panel of Triptych
Museum, Helsingborg
What would your ideal Christmas tree look like?

KERSTI'S BIRTHDAY, 1909
from *De Mina*, 1919
If you could have any birthday cake you could imagine, what would it look like?

MY FRIENDS, THE CARPENTER AND THE PAINTER, 1909
Frontispiece for *At Solsidan,* 1910
Not counting your mom or dad or grandparents, who are two of your best adult friends?

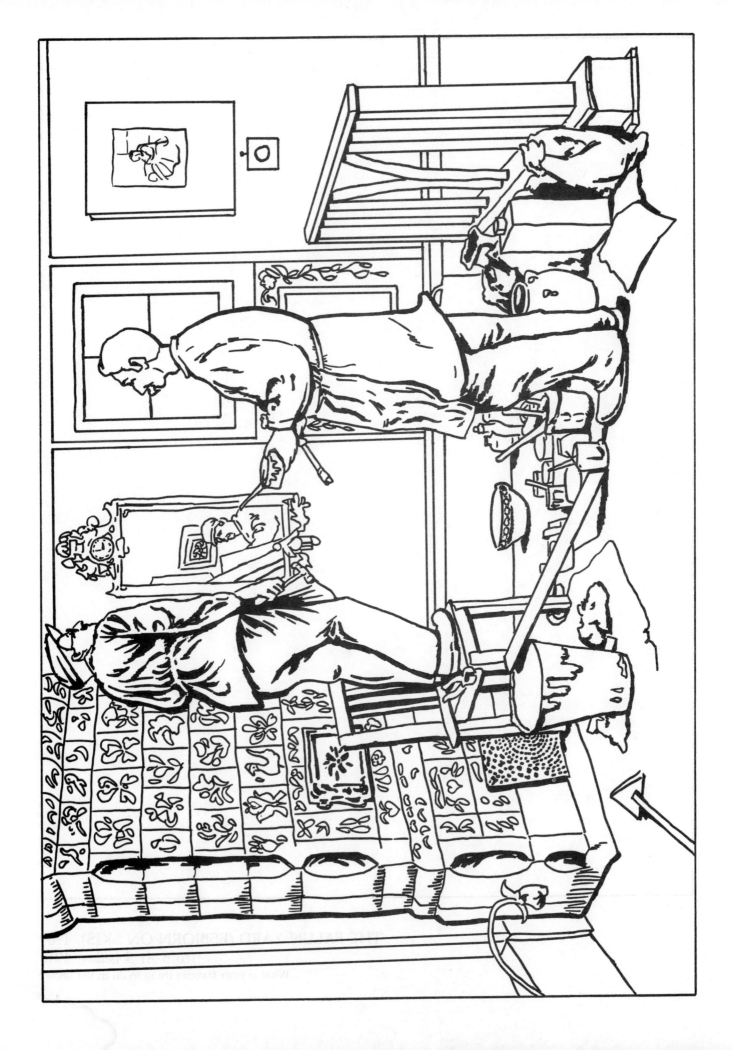

THE FALUN YARD (ESBJORN ON SKIS), 1909
from *At Solsidan*, 1910
What is your favorite thing to do in the snow?

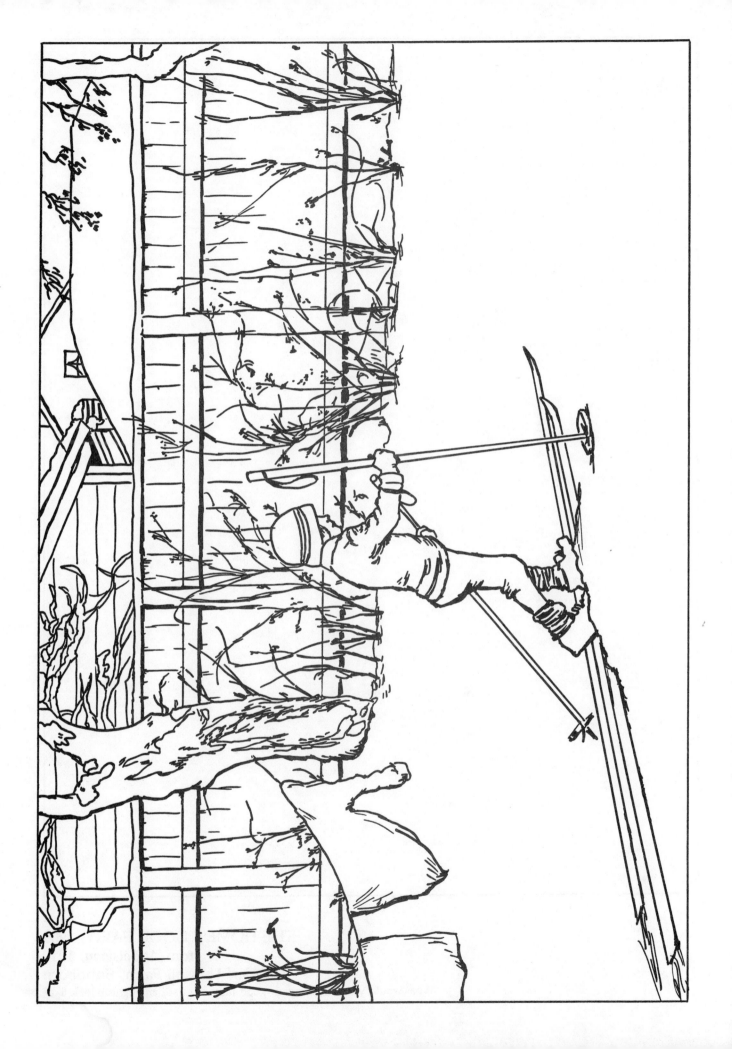

THE HOME'S GOOD FAIRY, 1909
from *At Solsidan*, 1910
The Carl Larsson Farm, Sundborn
What would you imagine your good fairy or guardian angel to look like?

WHERE I DO MY ETCHING, 1910
from *At Solsidan*, 1910

Etchings are art prints. The printer is standing at a printing press. Books are also printed
on printing presses. What would the cover of a book about you look like?

BREAKFAST IN THE OPEN, (Detail), Oil, 1910–1913
Norrkoping Museum
Have you ever eaten breakfast outside? How would you cook your food outside? What would you eat?

ROSALIND, 1911
from *Andras Barn*, 1913
If you could open any door in the world, who or what would you find behind it?

HILDA, 1911
from *Andras Barn*, 1913
Who would you like to write a letter to? Draw a picture of that person.

MATTS LARSSON, 1912
from *Andras Barn*, 1913
This was the grandson of the publisher Bonnier. What do you suppose Matts is thinking about?

UNTITLED, 1913
Frontispiece for *Andras Barn*, 1913
Look at these hats! What does your favorite hat look like?

ESBJORN READING ON THE VERANDA, 1918
Privately owned
Where is your favorite place to read?

Culpepper Press Coloring Books

*The Impressionists
Coloring Book*
By Andy Nelson
ISBN 0-929636-06-6
$5.95   96 pp   48 drawings

*The Carl Larsson
Coloring Book*
By Andy Nelson
ISBN 0-929636-07-4
$5.95   96 pp   45 drawings

To purchase additional Culpepper Press coloring books ask
your local bookstore to order it for you or send $5.95 per
copy plus $1.75 shipping and handling per order to:
Culpepper Press, 6921 Gordan Road, Siren, WI 54872.

Coming Spring 1991:
*The Renaissance Painters
Coloring Book*